KT-407-656

XB00 000000 8728

GRAPHIC DISCOVERIES

THE HISTORY OF FLIGHT

by Gary Jeffrey

FRANKLIN WATTS
LONDON•SYDNEY

First published in 2009 by Franklin Watts

Franklin Watts
338 Euston Road
London NW1 3BH

Franklin Watts Australia
Level 17/207 Kent Street
Sydney, NSW 2000

A CIP catalogue record for this book is available from the British Library.

Dewey number: 629.1'3'09

ISBN: 978 0 7496 9242 1

Franklin Watts is a division of Hachette Children's Books, an Hachette UK company.
www.hachette.co.uk

GRAPHIC DISCOVERIES: THE HISTORY OF FLIGHT produced for Franklin Watts
by David West Children's Books, 7 Princeton Court, 55 Felsham Road,
London SW15 1AZ

Designed and produced by
David West Children's Books

Editor: Gail Bushnell

Photo credits:
All photos courtesy of NASA

Printed in China

CONTENTS

EARLY DAYS

It is impossible to say when people first dreamed of flying. In ancient Greek mythology Daedalus and Icarus made wings from feathers. In the 15th century Leonardo da Vinci drew diagrams of flying machines. But it wasn't until 1783 that people first flew in an aircraft - a balloon designed by the Montgolfier brothers in France.

BALLOONING

The success of the Montgolfiers ensured that ballooning became popular in Europe in the 18th and 19th centuries. This lead to steam-powered airships filled with lighter-than-air hydrogen gas, such as Giffard's of 1852 and the French army's *La France* of 1884.

HEAVIER THAN AIR

The 1800s also saw people experimenting with gliders. Englishman Sir George Cayley had success with a glider that was piloted by his coachman. In France, Jean-Marie Le Bris made the first flight that rose from the ground, 'higher than departure', in 1856. A German, Otto Lilienthal, made over 2,000 glider flights before a flying accident killed him in 1896. The Wright brothers flew their propeller-driven plane near Kitty Hawk, North Carolina, on 17 December 1903.

On 21 November 1783, the first free flight was made by Pilâtre de Rozier and the Marquis d'Arlandes in a balloon invented by the Montgolfier brothers.

La France *was the first airship controlled by using electric motors.*

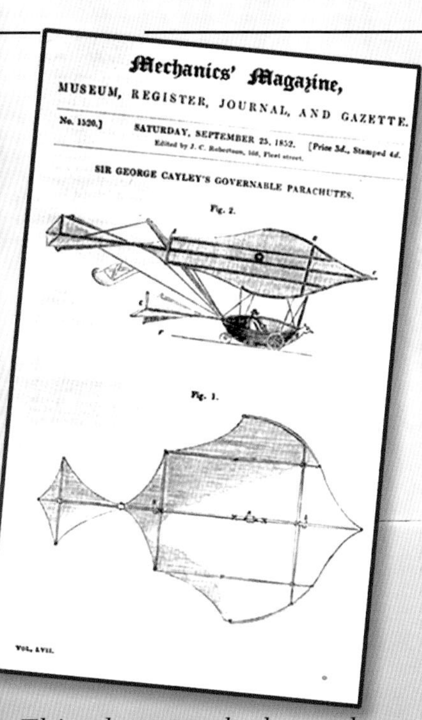

Mechanics' Magazine,

MUSEUM, REGISTER, JOURNAL, AND GAZETTE.

No. 1520.] SATURDAY, SEPTEMBER 25, 1852. [Price 3d., Stamped 4d.

Edited by J. C. Robertson, 166, Fleet street.

SIR GEORGE CAYLEY'S GOVERNABLE PARACHUTES.

Fig. 2.

Fig. 1.

VOL. LVII.

Sir George Cayley's glider (left) was the first to fly a person, in 1853.

Le Bris's L'Albatros artificiel *(below) was towed behind a horse on a beach. It reached a height of 100 metres.*

Otto Lilienthal was known as the Glider King. His gliders (above) were controlled and looked similar to hang gliders today.

This photograph shows the first powered flight of 36.5 metres in 12 seconds. Orville Wright is at the controls.

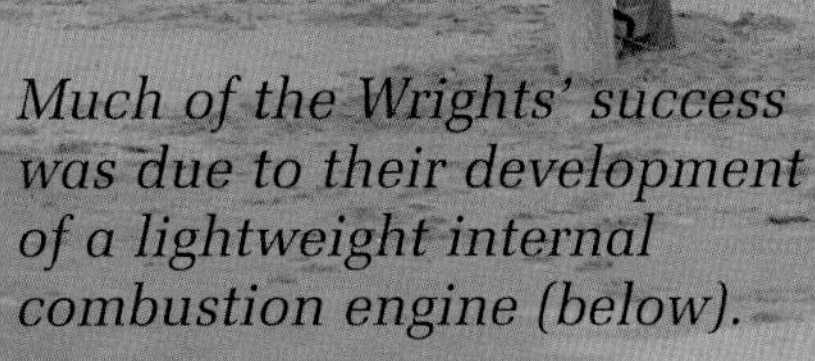

Much of the Wrights' success was due to their development of a lightweight internal combustion engine (below).

By watching birds and experimenting, the Wrights came up with the wing shape (a) that gave lift. As the wing moves through the air, the trailing edge (b) forces the air down (c), which forces the wing up, providing lift (d).

WAR AND EPIC FLIGHTS

The five decades following the Wrights' first flight saw the plane go from slow-flying crate to supersonic jet.

On 25 July 1909, Frenchman Louis Blériot became the first person to fly across the English Channel, between France and England.

1903 - 1910
Other designers began to make their own plane designs. In 1909, the first air show was held at Reims, France. Some of the greatest pioneers of flight took part, such as Curtiss, Blériot, Farman and Latham.

The Sopwith Camel, a fighter plane of WWI (below).

1911 - 1920
This decade saw the first aerial combat during World War I (1914–1918). In 1919, Alcock and Brown made the first nonstop flight across the Atlantic, in a Vickers Vimy.

Englishmen Alcock and Brown (below) took off from Newfoundland (bottom) and landed in Ireland on 15 June 1919, in just under 16 hours.

1921 - 1940
These two decades were known as the 'Golden Age' of flight. Epic flights were made by women as well as men. The first airliners appeared and planes were being made out of lightweight metals.

1941 - 1950
Huge steps in flight were made during this period. Jet planes and rocket planes were produced during World War II (1939 - 1945). By 1947, a plane flew faster than sound.

The Golden Age of flight produced many women pilots. American Amelia Earhart (right) was the first woman to fly solo across the Atlantic in 1932. She disappeared when attempting to fly around the world in 1937 in a Lockheed Electra (below).

American Charles Lindbergh (above) became famous for his nonstop solo flight across the Atlantic from New York to Paris in 1927.

During World War II, Germany produced the first jet fighter - the Messerschmitt Me 262 (left) and the first rocket-powered fighter - the Messerschmitt Me 163 Komet (below).

On 14 October 1947, American Chuck Yeager became the first person to fly faster than the speed of sound in the Bell X-1. Planes had become supersonic!

THE WRIGHT BROTHERS

"ONLY THIS TIME HE GOT CAUGHT IN MIDAIR BY A STRONG UPWIND, UNABLE TO MOVE."

"SUDDENLY THE WIND DIED AWAY."

"THE FALL BROKE HIS SPINE."
KRUMP!

"HIS LAST WORDS WERE... SACRIFICES MUST BE MADE..."

ON 29 AUGUST, AMERICAN ENGINEER OCTAVE CHANUTE FLEW A NEW TYPE OF GLIDER A DISTANCE OF 106 METRES.

THE NEWS CHEERED THE WRIGHTS, BUT THEY WERE STILL BOTHERED BY LILIENTHAL'S TRAGIC END...
I DON'T GET IT. HE WAS A MASTER PILOT - HE MADE TWO THOUSAND FLIGHTS IN SIXTEEN DIFFERENT GLIDERS.
LILIENTHAL DIED BECAUSE HE WAS AT THE **MERCY** OF THE WIND.
UNLIKE A BIRD, HE HAD NO EFFECTIVE WAY TO MANOEUVRE HIMSELF IN THOSE AIR CURRENTS.
SIMPLY TRYING TO SHIFT HIS WEIGHT AROUND IN A HARNESS WASN'T ENOUGH.

HE DIDN'T HAVE CONTROL!

OVER THE NEXT TWO YEARS, THE WRIGHTS CONSIDERED THE PROBLEM...
LOOK AT THE BUZZARD.

SEE HOW HE MOVES HIS WING TIPS IN OPPOSITE DIRECTIONS TO CORRECT HIS FLIGHT.
ROTATING LIKE A LIVING WINDMILL!
WILBUR WAS INTRIGUED AND, IN MAY 1899, WROTE TO THE SMITHSONIAN FOR A LIST OF AERONAUTICAL BOOKS...
"...I WISH TO FIND OUT ALL THAT IS ALREADY KNOWN AND IF POSSIBLE ADD MY MITE TO HELP THE FUTURE PERSON WHO WILL GAIN FINAL SUCCESS..."
BUT WHEN THE PAMPHLETS CAME...
MAXIM, CHANUTE, CALEY - THESE MEN HAVEN'T ANY IDEAS ABOUT *CONTROLLING* FLIGHT. THEIR ONLY INTEREST IS IN GETTING OFF THE GROUND!

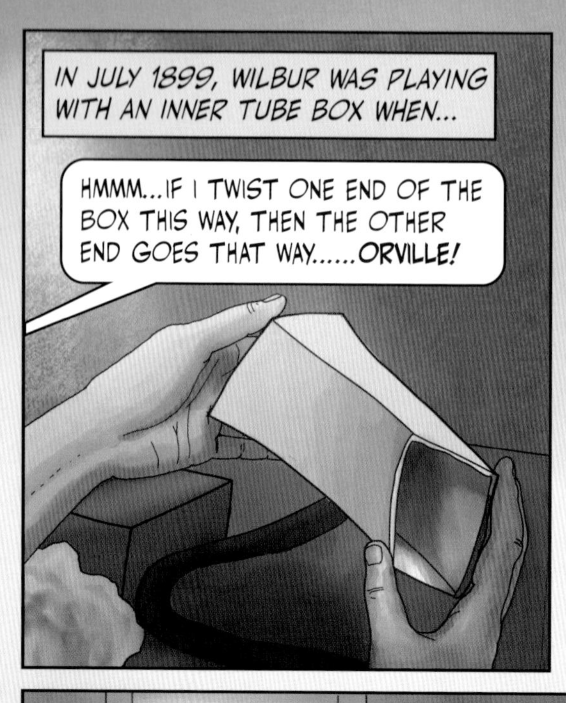
IN JULY 1899, WILBUR WAS PLAYING WITH AN INNER TUBE BOX WHEN...
HMMM...IF I TWIST ONE END OF THE BOX THIS WAY, THEN THE OTHER END GOES THAT WAY......ORVILLE!

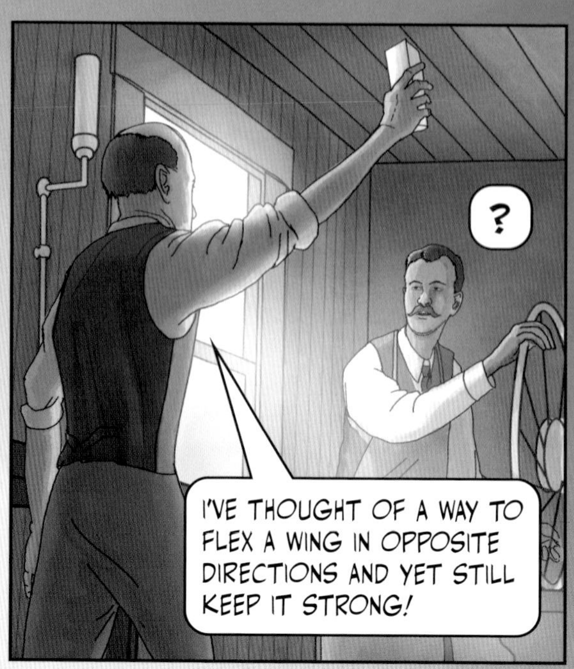
?
I'VE THOUGHT OF A WAY TO FLEX A WING IN OPPOSITE DIRECTIONS AND YET STILL KEEP IT STRONG!

USING CHANUTE'S GLIDER DESIGN, THEY BUILT THE FIRST EVER KITE TO HAVE...

...WING WARPING CONTROLS.
SHE'S ALOFT!

SWOOOOOOSH!
IT WORKS!
DUCK!
HEY! CUT IT OUT!

THAT NIGHT ORVILLE AGAIN LAY IN A FEVER, ONLY THIS TIME IT WASN'T TYPHOID.
HE DREAMED HE WAS ON THE KITE, FAR ABOVE THE EARTH.
HE FELT EXHILARATED AND, LIKE THE BIRDS, HE WAS FREE TO GO ANYWHERE...
ON 13 MAY 1900, WILBUR WROTE A LETTER TO CHANUTE...
"...I HAVE BEEN AFFLICTED WITH THE BELIEF THAT FLIGHT IS POSSIBLE TO MAN. MY DISEASE HAS INCREASED IN SEVERITY AND I FEEL THAT IT WILL SOON COST ME AN INCREASED AMOUNT OF MONEY IF NOT MY LIFE..."
HE STATED THEIR INTENTION - TO BUILD A MAN-CARRYING GLIDER TO TEST IN A SUITABLE PLACE...

EARLY OCTOBER 1900, KILL DEVIL HILLS, KITTY HAWK, NORTH CAROLINA.
READY?
THE EXPOSED COAST WAS GOOD AND WINDY. THE SOFT DUNES WOULD CUSHION ANY FALL.
THE GLIDER FLEW OVER 122 METRES BUT DIDN'T GO VERY HIGH OFF THE GROUND.

ENCOURAGED, THEY RETURNED TO DAYTON...
WE NEED TO GET MORE LIFT OUT OF THE NEXT DESIGN.
WE COULD TRY MAKING THE WINGS BIGGER, FOR STARTERS.
WHEN THEY TESTED THE NEW GLIDER IN JULY 1901, IT FLEW EVEN LOWER...
GET UP! GET UP!

WHAT'S MORE, IT WAS DANGEROUSLY UNSTABLE...
DARN THING KEEPS TRYING TO DIVE INTO THE GROUND!
SOMETHING'S DEFINITELY WRONG!
IT HAS TO BE OUR INFORMATION – LILIENTHAL'S AND CHANUTE'S CALCULATIONS FOR THE WING SHAPE MUST BE INACCURATE.
DOWNCAST, THEY PACKED UP AND LEFT.
ORVILLE, I DON'T THINK MAN WILL FLY FOR ANOTHER THOUSAND YEARS!
HOWEVER, WHEN THEY GOT HOME...
WHY DON'T WE TRY DOING SOME 'AERO' RESEARCH OF OUR OWN?

THEY BEGAN WITH SIMPLE HOMEMADE EXPERIMENTS...
THIS IS ALL VERY WELL, BUT I THINK OUR METHODS NEED TO BE MORE... SCIENTIFIC.
SO THEY BUILT A WIND TUNNEL...
...AND TESTED HUNDREDS OF AIRFOILS (WING SHAPES) UNTIL...
...FINALLY!
HMM...I'VE WORKED OUT THAT OUR WINGS NEED TO BE LONGER AND THINNER!
AND THIS IS IT - THE AEROFOIL THAT WILL GIVE THE MOST LIFT!

IN SEPTEMBER 1902, THEY TESTED A NEW GLIDER...
IT FLIES BEAUTIFULLY, EVEN IN THIS CROSSWIND!
YES, I CAN FEEL HOW MUCH SHE WANTS TO CLIMB!
THEY HAD ADDED A FIXED RUDDER TO IMPROVE STABILITY.
ON SEPTEMBER 22, ORVILLE WAS LAUNCHED INTO SPACE...
I'M GOING TO HEAD FOR THE CAMP!
OH, NO! HE'S ABOUT TO GO WELL-DIGGING!

IT WAS THE WRIGHTS' NAME FOR A CRASH LANDING.
KERRRUMP!
WHAT HAPPENED?
UGH, IT JUST STOPPED IN MIDAIR AND THEN SPUN INTO THE GROUND!
UNLIKE LILIENTHAL, ORVILLE WAS UNHURT.
THEY REBUILT THE GLIDER, MADE THE RUDDER MOVABLE AND CONNECTED IT TO THE WING WARPING CONTROLS.
SOON...
I'VE MADE SIX HUNDRED FEET, WITH GOOD CONTROL!
IT WAS TIME TO FIND AN ENGINE.

BACK IN DAYTON THEY SENT LETTERS OUT TO AUTOMOBILE MAKERS, BUT...
...THEY CAN ALL MAKE A LIGHTWEIGHT ENGINE, BUT NONE OF THEM WILL TOOL UP JUST TO DO A ONE-OFF!

WHY DON'T WE MAKE OUR OWN? WE CAN GET CHARLIE TO HELP US.
CHARLES TAYLOR WAS A TALENTED LOCAL MECHANIC.

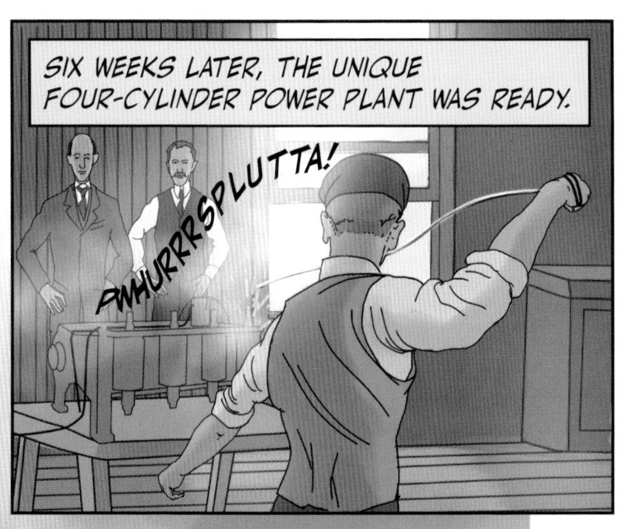
SIX WEEKS LATER, THE UNIQUE FOUR-CYLINDER POWER PLANT WAS READY.
PWHURRRSPLUTTA!

BLATTA-BLATTA-BLATTA
IT'S TERRIFIC! NOW WE JUST NEED TO MAKE THE SPINNERS!

USING THEIR TEST DATA, THE WRIGHTS CRAFTED TWO PROPELLERS THAT HAD EDGES LIKE MINI-WINGS, TWISTING IN TOWARDS THE CENTRE.

BY LATE SUMMER OF 1903...
THAT'S IT, WE'RE ALL FINSHED HERE.
LIKE THE GLIDERS, THE AIRFRAME WOULD BE PUT TOGETHER AT KITTY HAWK.

17 DECEMBER,
10:30 A.M...
ON THREE! ONE-
TWO-THREE...
KRANKKUWEEEEEEEEEEEE
KER-BLATTA-BLATTA-BLATTA-BLATTA
THEY HAD ENDURED ELEVEN WEEKS OF DELAYS AND PROBLEMS. TODAY THE WEATHER CONDITIONS WERE NOT IDEAL, BUT THE BROTHERS HAD DECIDED TO TAKE A CHANCE.

IT WAS ORVILLE'S TURN TO PILOT THE 'WHOPPER FLYING MACHINE' AFTER AN UNSUCCESSFUL ATTEMPT BY WILBUR THREE DAYS EARLIER.
WIND SPEED IS TWENTY-SEVEN MILES PER HOUR!
RUDDER WORKING ...WING WARPING WORKING...

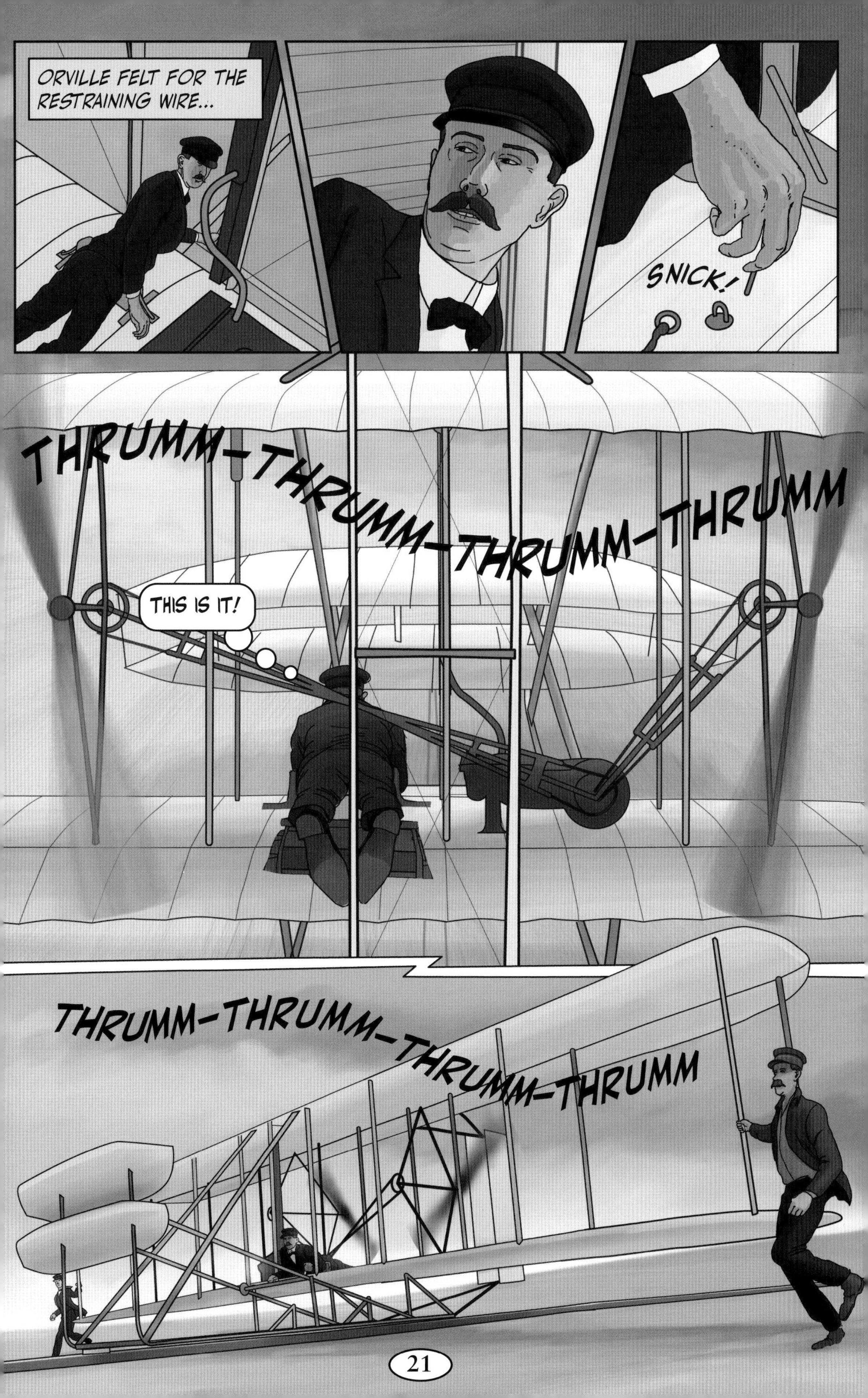
ORVILLE FELT FOR THE RESTRAINING WIRE...
SNICK!
THRUMM-THRUMM-THRUMM-THRUMM-THRUMM
THIS IS IT!
THRUMM-THRUMM-THRUMM-THRUMM

COME ON ORVILLE!
...YES!
THRUMM-THRUMM-THRUMM-THRUMM
HOOORAAAAY!
ORVILLE FOUGHT TO ADJUST THE FLYER'S HORRIBLY OVERSENSITIVE CONTROLS.
THE FLYER MAY HAVE BEEN UNSTEADY, BUT FOR 12 SECONDS IT FLEW...

...AND THEN LANDED SAFELY.
ONE HUNDRED AND TWENTY FEET!
AND YOU CONTROLLED IT ALL THE WAY, BROTHER!
THEY DID THREE MORE FLIGHTS, WITH WILBUR'S LAST REACHING OVER 244 METRES.
AS THEY PREPARED FOR A FINAL FLIGHT, A GUST OF WIND CAUGHT THE FLYER. BUT IT DIDN'T MATTER BECAUSE...
THEY DONE IT! THEY DONE IT! DARN ME IF THEY AIN'T FLEW!
THE WORLD WOULD SOON LEARN OF THE WRIGHTS' ACHIEVEMENT AND FIND ITSELF CHANGED...FOREVER.
THE END

THE SPIRIT OF ST LOUIS

THREE MONTHS EARLIER, AT ROOSEVELT FIELD, FRENCH FLYING ACE RENÉ FONCK HAD FIRED UP THE ENGINES OF HIS SIKORSKY S35.
BRRRRAAAAAAGH
HE WAS TRYING TO WIN THE $25,000 ORTEIG PRIZE FOR THE FIRST NONSTOP TRANSATLANTIC FLIGHT FROM NEW YORK TO PARIS.
ON TAKEOFF, THE UNDERCARRIAGE OF HIS FUEL-LADEN AIRPLANE GAVE WAY...
KAROOM!
TWO CREWMEN DIED.
IN LATE DECEMBER, LINDBERGH MET WITH THE ST LOUIS CHAMBER OF COMMERCE...
I THINK THAT THE TRANSATLANTIC CROSSING CAN ONLY BE DONE BY A LIGHTWEIGHT, SINGLE-ENGINED AIRCRAFT.

FEBRUARY 1927.

IT WILL COST $10,500 AND TAKE THREE MONTHS TO BUILD.

RYAN AIRCRAFT, SAN DIEGO, CALIFORNIA.

WE CAN USE THE TAILPLANE AND THE WING STRUTS FROM THE M1 HERE, BUT EVERYTHING ELSE WILL HAVE TO BE BUILT FROM SCRATCH.
DONALD HALL WAS CHIEF DESIGNER.
I'LL NEED IT DONE IN TWO MONTHS AND I'VE GOT SOME SPECIFIC DESIGN REQUESTS.
HE WAS DETERMINED TO MAKE THE AIRCRAFT AS LIGHT AS POSSIBLE, EVEN IF IT MEANT...
FLYING SOLO?
THAT WAS NEVER PART OF THE DEAL!
HOW ARE YOU GOING TO STAY AWAKE BY YOURSELF FOR FORTY HOURS?
EASILY - IT JUST TAKES CONCENTRATION.
WORK ON THE 'NEW YORK PLANE' RUSHED AHEAD, WITH LINDBERGH INVOLVED AT EVERY STAGE...
I NEED TO SIT *BEHIND* THE FOUR HUNDRED GALLON FUEL TANK.
BUT THAT WILL BLOCK YOUR FORWARD VISION!
I DON'T WANT TO BE *CRUSHED* BY THAT BIG TANK IF I CRASH.

THEY HAD BETTER AIRCRAFT, MORE MONEY AND THEY WERE READY TO GO.

Davis & Wooster in 'American Legion'.

Nungesser & Coli in 'White Bird'.

Clarence Chamberlin in 'Miss Columbia'.

Richard E. Byrd in 'America'.

LINDBERGH WAS LABELLED 'A FLYING FOOL'.

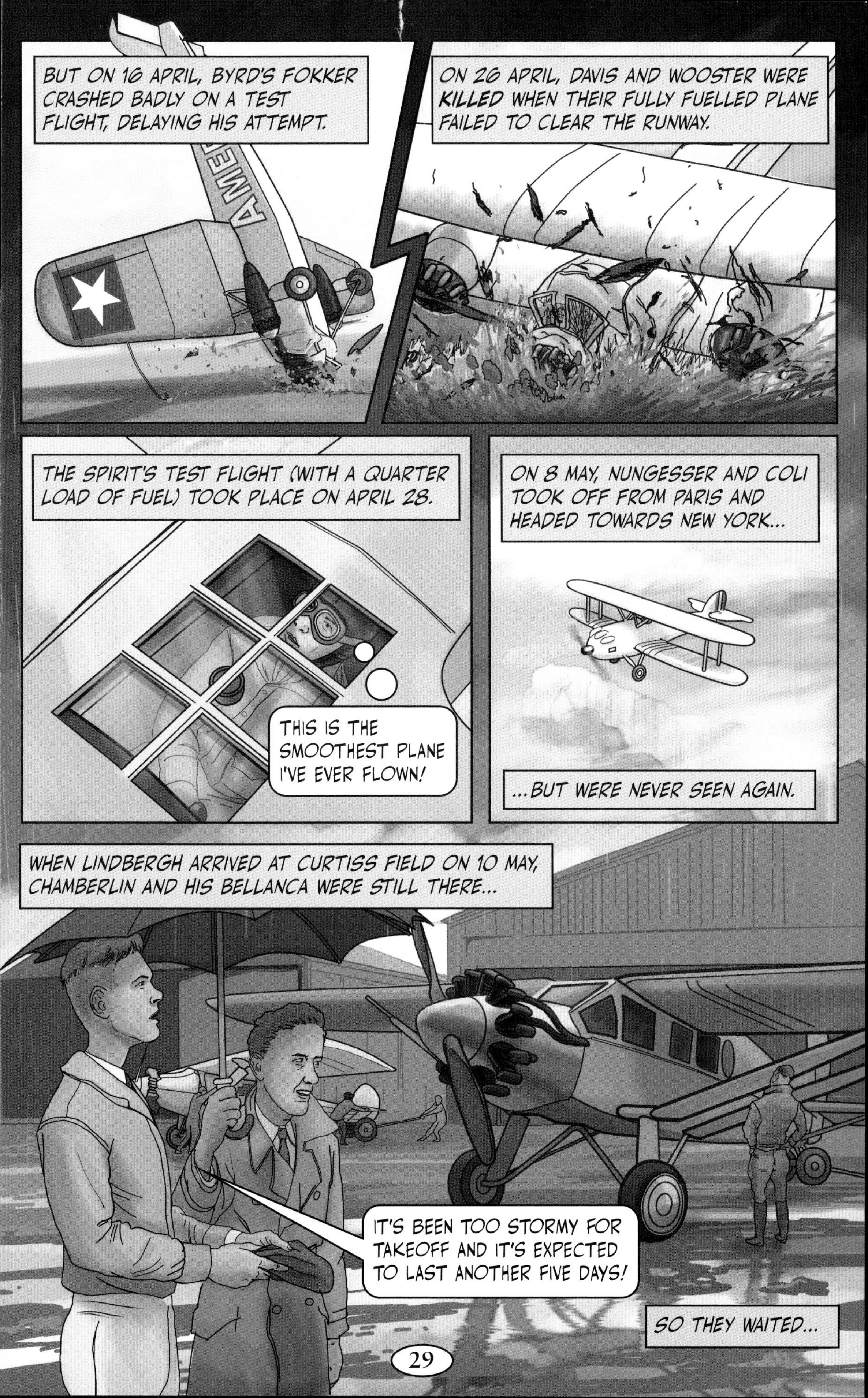
BUT ON 16 APRIL, BYRD'S FOKKER CRASHED BADLY ON A TEST FLIGHT, DELAYING HIS ATTEMPT.
AMER
ON 26 APRIL, DAVIS AND WOOSTER WERE **KILLED** WHEN THEIR FULLY FUELLED PLANE FAILED TO CLEAR THE RUNWAY.
THE SPIRIT'S TEST FLIGHT (WITH A QUARTER LOAD OF FUEL) TOOK PLACE ON APRIL 28.
THIS IS THE SMOOTHEST PLANE I'VE EVER FLOWN!
ON 8 MAY, NUNGESSER AND COLI TOOK OFF FROM PARIS AND HEADED TOWARDS NEW YORK...
...BUT WERE NEVER SEEN AGAIN.
WHEN LINDBERGH ARRIVED AT CURTISS FIELD ON 10 MAY, CHAMBERLIN AND HIS BELLANCA WERE STILL THERE...
IT'S BEEN TOO STORMY FOR TAKEOFF AND IT'S EXPECTED TO LAST ANOTHER FIVE DAYS!
SO THEY WAITED...

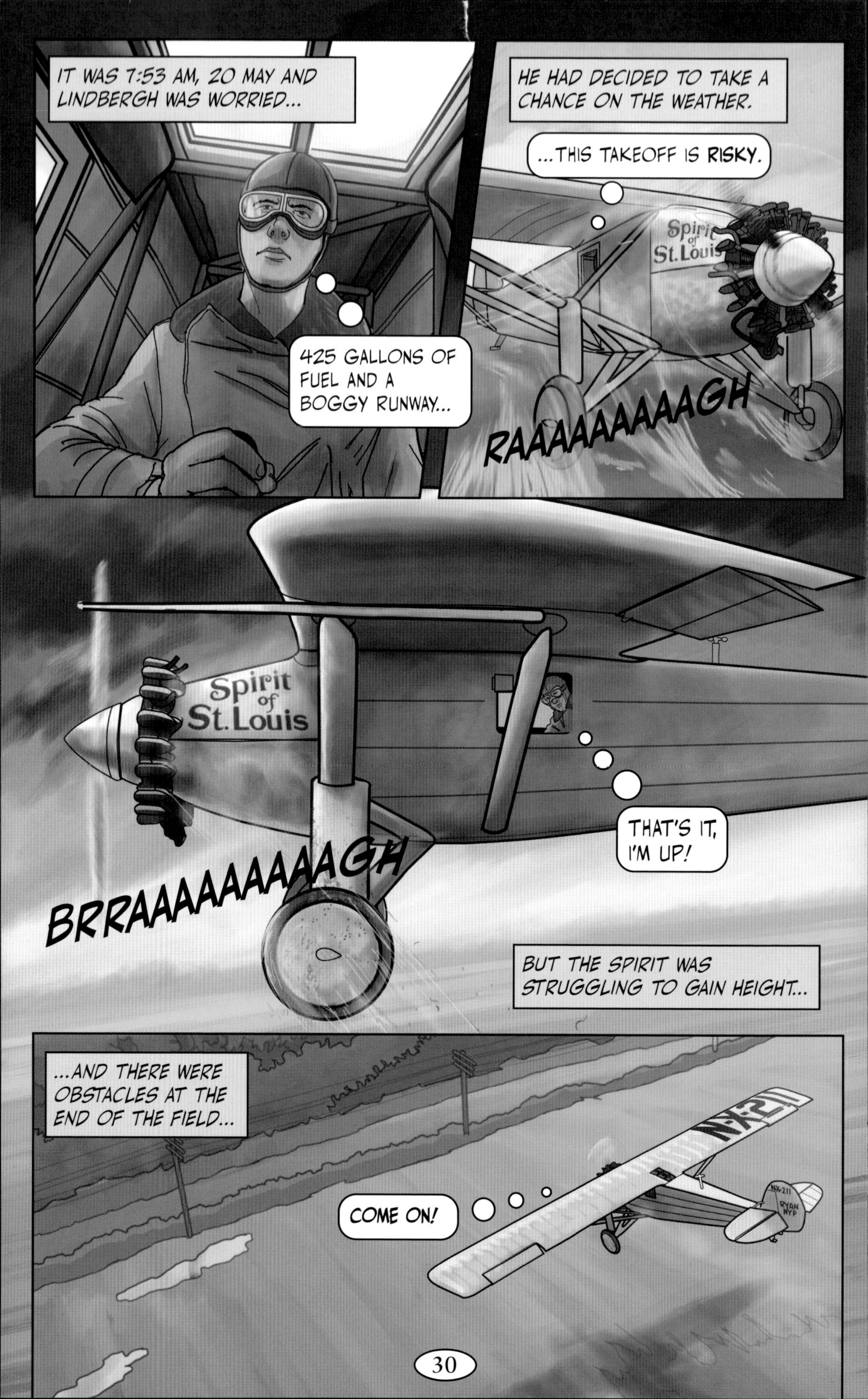
IT WAS 7:53 AM, 20 MAY AND LINDBERGH WAS WORRIED...
425 GALLONS OF FUEL AND A BOGGY RUNWAY...
HE HAD DECIDED TO TAKE A CHANCE ON THE WEATHER.
...THIS TAKEOFF IS RISKY.
Spirit of St. Louis
RAAAAAAAAAGH
Spirit of St. Louis
THAT'S IT, I'M UP!
BRRAAAAAAAAAGH
BUT THE SPIRIT WAS STRUGGLING TO GAIN HEIGHT...
...AND THERE WERE OBSTACLES AT THE END OF THE FIELD...
COME ON!
NX-211
NX-211
RYAN NYP

LINDBERGH GAVE IT FULL THROTTLE...
N-X-211
HE'S AWAY!
MUUWHAAAAAAAH!
GO LINDY!
LATER, OVER LONG ISLAND SOUND, THE LAST ESCORT PLANE DROPPED AWAY.
GOOD LUCK, LONE EAGLE!
Spirit of St. Louis
HE WAS ON HIS OWN...
ONLY 2,450 MILES TO GO.
OFF ST. JOHN'S, NEWFOUNDLAND, 8:15 PM...
ICEBERGS!
MUST BE ALMOST ZERO OUT THERE.
THEN...
RAIN! AND THE CLOUDS ARE TOO HIGH TO FLY OVER.
Spirit of St. Louis
GOING TO HAVE TO FLY THROUGH INSTEAD.

10:15 PM...
5
RPM
20
10
15
ENGINE'S HAVING TO WORK REAL HARD TO MAINTAIN ALTITUDE...
...THE ICY RAIN MUST BE BUILDING UP ON MY WINGS.
I'LL HAVE TO TURN BACK AND FLY AROUND THIS STORM.
KRRRRARRK!
AS THE HOURS TICKED BY...
NNNNAAGH!...MUST STAY AWAKE...STAY AWAKE...
THEN, 27 HOURS AFTER TAKING OFF...
THE IRISH COAST! ONLY SIX HUNDRED MILES TO PARIS!

OVER DEAUVILLE, FRANCE...
THEY MUST BE THE BEACONS OF THE PARIS - LONDON AIRWAY!
LE BOURGET, PARIS, 10:24 PM.
OH BOY, THAT'S SOME WELCOMING CROWD!
LINDBERGH! LINDBERGH!
QUICKLY, THIS WAY!
HE WAS RESCUED FROM THE HAPPY CROWD BY SOME FRENCH AIRMEN.
I...I WASN'T PREPARED FOR THIS. I DIDN'T EVEN BRING A VISA!
HA, HA, DON'T WORRY, MONSIEUR LINDBERGH. ALL FRANCE IS YOURS!
LINDBERGH'S EPIC FLIGHT FOUNDED THE MODERN AIRLINE INDUSTRY. THE END

BREAKING THE SOUND BARRIER

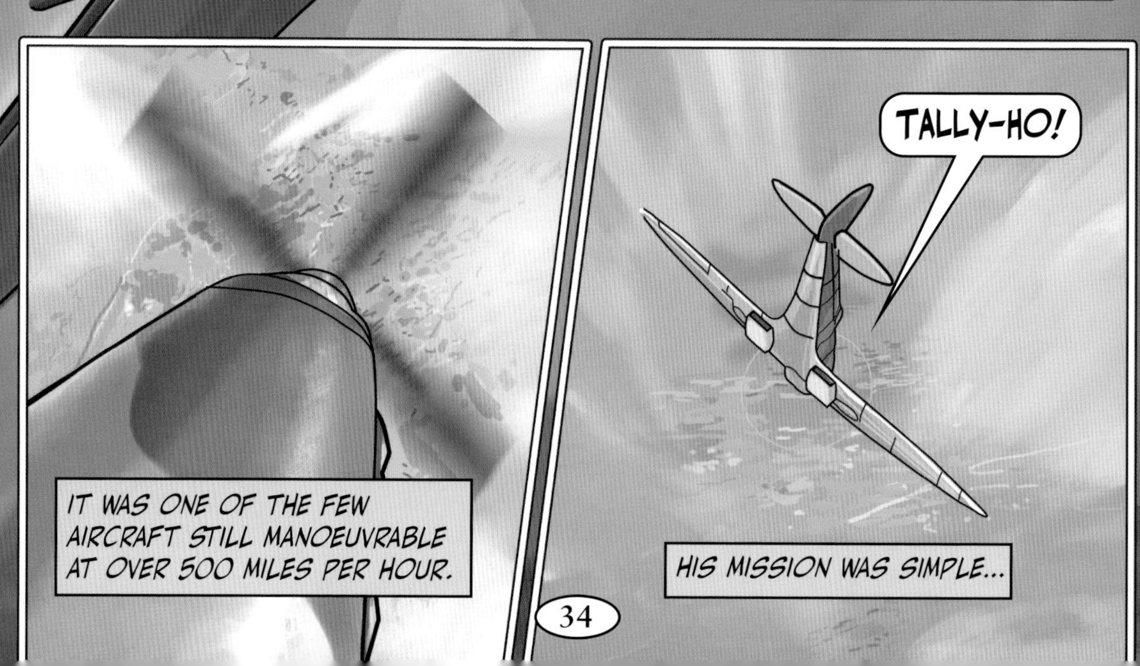

TO FLY AS NEAR AS POSSIBLE...
FIVE HUNDRED AND SEVENTY – NOSE IS DIPPING!
...TO THE SPEED OF SOUND.
FIVE HUNDRED AND NINETY – NOSE REALLY PITCHING DOWN NOW, CORRECTING...
UGH...CONTROLS ARE NOT RESPONDING!
...NOT RESPONDING!
SIX HUNDRED MILES AN HOUR! THIS IS IT - I'M GOING TO HIT THE GROUND!
AAAAAAARGH!
KAABOOM!
KERWAAAANG!

OKAY, OKAY, I'VE GOT HER!
I'M COMING IN.
MARTINDALE WAS LUCKY. CONVENTIONAL AIRCRAFT HAD REACHED THEIR LIMITS.
IN SAN DIEGO, CALIFORNIA...
THIS BULLET IS THE ONLY SUPERSONIC* OBJECT WE HAVE ANY INFORMATION ON.
*MACH 1 - THE SPEED OF SOUND - 1,235 KILOMETRES PER HOUR.
OKAY! THEN LET'S COPY THIS SHAPE!
BELL AIRCRAFT HAD BEEN CONTRACTED TO DESIGN A SUPERSONIC MILITARY AIRPLANE.
BY OCTOBER 1945 THEY HAD BUILT A FULL-SIZE MOCK-UP...
IT'S DESIGNED TO BE AIR-LAUNCHED...

"...THE PILOT WILL SIMPLY
GLIDE THE AIRCRAFT
BACK TO BASE..."

BY DECEMBER 1946, BELL HAD BEGUN FLIGHT TRIALS OF THE COMPLETED 'EXPERIMENTAL SUPERSONIC-1' AT MUROC ARMY AIRFIELD IN LOS ANGELES.

WE'RE TAKING OVER THE XS-1 TEST PROGRAMME!
COLONEL ALBERT BOYD HAD LOBBIED HARD FOR CONTROL.
US
NOW I JUST NEED A PILOT -SOMEONE WHO CAN STAY FOCUSED UNDER PRESSURE...
HIS FIRST CHOICE WAS CAPTAIN CHARLES E. YEAGER.
U.S. AIR FORCE
HOW'S SHE RUNNING, CHUCK?
NOT BAD. STILL SEEMS A TAD UNDERPOWERED, THOUGH...
THE 24-YEAR-OLD MAINTENANCE OFFICER COULD OUTFLY EVERY OTHER PILOT ON THE BASE.
BUT BOYD HAD CONCERNS...
CHUCK, THE XS-1 IS BASICALLY A FLYING BOMB.
I SHOULD REALLY BE CHOOSING A PILOT WHO DOSEN'T HAVE A WIFE AND KID.
NO. IT'S OKAY, SIR...

...JUST MEANS I'LL BE MORE CAUTIOUS THAN A SINGLE MAN!
THE SKIES ABOVE MUROC, THREE MONTHS LATER...
READY WHEN YOU ARE, CAPTAIN YEAGER.
THIS HAS ALMOST BECOME ROUTINE!
IT WAS HIS SIXTH POWERED TEST.
TANKS ARE PRESSURISED.
OKAY, SIR, WE ARE READY TO DROP.
WITH EACH FLIGHT THE MACH NUMBER HAD BEEN SLOWLY INCREASED.
TODAY HE WAS TO GAIN MACH .95...
AIRSPEED IS STEADY AT 250.

CLICK
CLICK
TIME TO LIGHT THIS BABY UP!
SHOOOOOOOOOOM!
MACH
MACH
MACH

MACH .94 – NOSE IS PITCHING DOWNWARD – I AM CORRECTING...
THE CONTROLS ARE NOT RESPONDING!
SHUTTING DOWN ENGINES AND RETURNING TO BASE.
YEAGER SPOKE TO CHIEF ENGINEER JACK RIDLEY....
...AND WHEN I TRIED TO CORRECT THE ANGLE OF PITCH, THE CONTROLS JUST LOCKED OUT!
HMMM...SHOCK WAVES FROM THE AIRCRAFT COULD BE 'PINNING' THE ELEVATORS DOWN.
A SOLUTION MIGHT BE TO MAKE THE WHOLE STABILISER MOVABLE.
AN 'ALL FLYING TAIL' – GREAT, LET'S TRY IT!
THE CHANGE WORKED AND ON THE NEXT FLIGHT MACH .96 WAS GAINED.
MACH .98 IS NEXT!

14 OCTOBER. IN THE X-1, AT MACH .96...
YEOW! MY SIDE!
YEAGER HAD RECENTLY BROKEN A COUPLE OF RIBS IN A RIDING ACCIDENT, BUT HAD KEPT IT A SECRET.
HE FOCUSED...
I'VE GOT ENOUGH FUEL LEFT TO RELIGHT MY FOURTH ROCKET...
...WHAT THE HECK, LET'S GO FOR IT!
FWOOOOOSH!
THE MACH METER'S JUMPED OFF THE SCALE!
YEAGER TO BASE, DID YOU READ THAT?
HEY, WAS THAT A THUNDERCLAP?

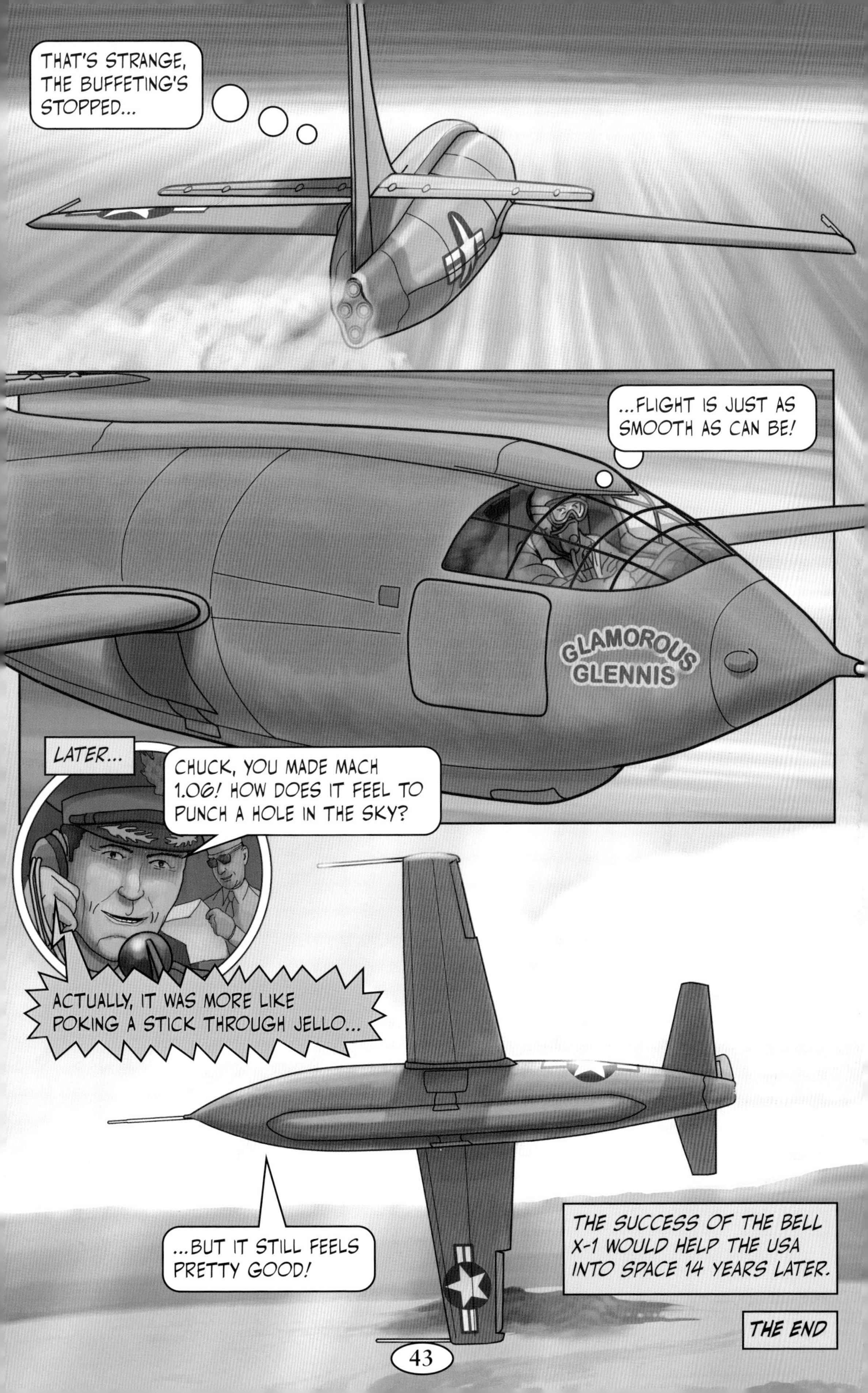
THAT'S STRANGE, THE BUFFETING'S STOPPED...
...FLIGHT IS JUST AS SMOOTH AS CAN BE!
GLAMOROUS GLENNIS
LATER...
CHUCK, YOU MADE MACH 1.06! HOW DOES IT FEEL TO PUNCH A HOLE IN THE SKY?
ACTUALLY, IT WAS MORE LIKE POKING A STICK THROUGH JELLO...
...BUT IT STILL FEELS PRETTY GOOD!
THE SUCCESS OF THE BELL X-1 WOULD HELP THE USA INTO SPACE 14 YEARS LATER.
THE END

BIGGER AND FASTER

The second half of the 20th century saw further developments in flight, from hovering planes to radar invisible bombers.

INTO THE 21ST CENTURY

Air transport continues to grow, along with the size of the airliners, which carry more people than ever before. Computers have made the biggest impact on plane design. Today, designers make planes that can only fly with the aid of computers. Flying wings, like the B2 stealth bomber, could not fly without computer assistance. In the future, air battles will be fought with pilotless planes - flown by remote control.

In 1957, the Short SC.1 *was the first plane to take off and land vertically (top). This led to the* Harrier Jump Jet *(above).*

The French engineer Paul Cornu built and flew the first helicopter in 1907. However, it was Ukrainian Igor Sikorsky (above left) who produced the first commercial helicopter, the Sikorsky R-4B, *in 1942.*

The first jet airliner was the de Havilland Comet. *First flown in 1949, it went into service in 1952.*

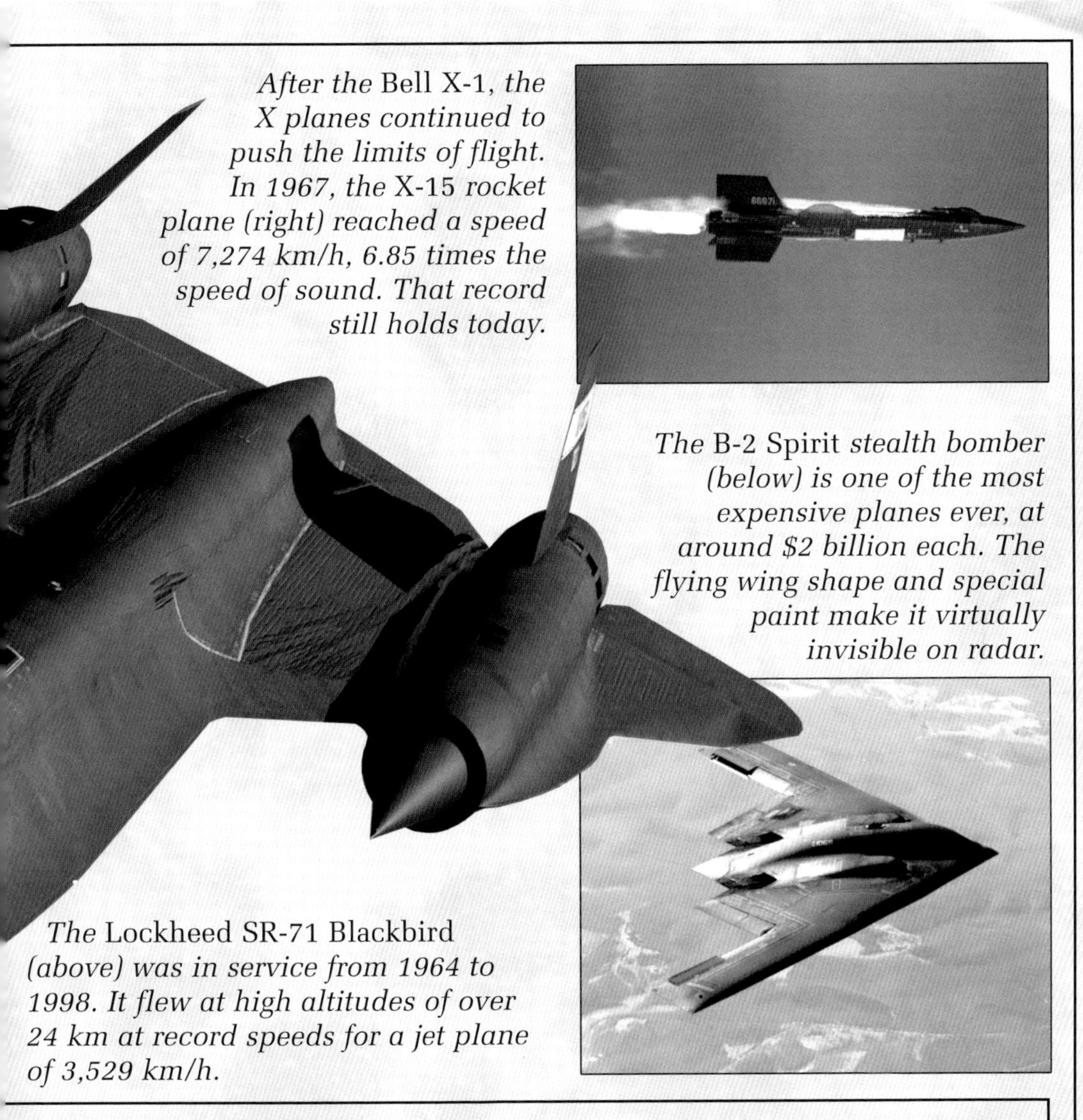

After the Bell X-1, the X planes continued to push the limits of flight. In 1967, the X-15 rocket plane (right) reached a speed of 7,274 km/h, 6.85 times the speed of sound. That record still holds today.

The B-2 Spirit stealth bomber (below) is one of the most expensive planes ever, at around $2 billion each. The flying wing shape and special paint make it virtually invisible on radar.

The Lockheed SR-71 Blackbird (above) was in service from 1964 to 1998. It flew at high altitudes of over 24 km at record speeds for a jet plane of 3,529 km/h.

Concorde, the world's only supersonic airliner, made its final flight in November 2003.

The world's biggest airliner, the Airbus A380, can carry up to 880 people.

GLOSSARY

aeronautics The scientific study of travel through the Earth's atmosphere.

airliner A large passenger airplane.

airship A type of aircraft that consists of a long gas-filled structure with an engine to make it move and a roomlike structure underneath for passengers or cargo.

altitude Height, usually above sea level.

Atlantic Ocean The body of water separating the American continent from the European and African continents.

civilisation A people and their society and culture.

crosswind A wind blowing across the path of a vehicle or aircraft.

glider A small airplane with no engine, kept in flight by rising currents of warm air.

harness A support consisting of various straps for holding something to the body.

hydrogen A colourless, odourless, tasteless gas that burns quickly in air.

inner tube An inflatable rubber tube inside a tyre, e.g. a bicycle tyre.

internal combustion engine An engine that produces power by burning a mixture of fuel and air within an enclosed space inside the engine.

lightweight Something that does not weigh very much.

Mach The ratio of the speed of an object such as an aircraft to the speed of sound in the same medium.

manoeuvre To move something accurately and with skill.

mite A small contribution.

monoplane An airplane with one set of wings.

pioneer Someone who breaks new ground in something.

power drive A downward plunge of an aircraft accelerated by both gravity and engine power.

propeller A device consisting of a shaft with rotating blades to drive forward or steer an aircraft.

radar A system for detecting the position, speed and direction of movement of distant objects.

supersonic Faster than the speed of sound.

wing warping controls A system of pulleys and cables to twist the trailing edges of the wings of an airplane in opposite directions.

FOR MORE INFORMATION

ORGANISATIONS

RAF Museum London
Grahame Park Way
London NW9 5LL
020 8205 2266
E-mail: london@rafmuseum.org
Website: http://www.rafmuseum.org.uk

Imperial War Museum
Duxford
Cambridgeshire
CB22 4QR
01223 835000
E-mail: duxford@iwm.org.uk
Website: http://duxford.iwm.org.uk

FURTHER READING

Graham, Ian. *The Wright Brothers and the Science of Flight* (Explosion Zone). Brighton: Book House, 2003.

Grant, Reg. *Flight*. London: Dorling Kindersley, 2007.

Lewis, Simon. *Adventures in the Air* (Difficult and Dangerous). London: Franklin Watts, 2008.

Nahum, Andrew. *Flying Machine* (Eyewitness). London: Dorling Kindersley, 2003.

Steen Hansen, Ole. *Aircraft* (Twentieth Century Inventions). London: Wayland, 1997.

INDEX